Foreword

The activities in these books will stimulate children's intere
vocabulary and will encourage further reading and writing

This book specialises in language; it covers nouns, verbs, adjectives, adverbs, prepositions, contractions, spoonerisms, analogies, similes, tautology and punctuation.

Contents

Cross-reference

Our language is made up of words. These words do various jobs. Words that name things are called NOUNS. The things that they give names to can sometimes be seen or touched.

Sometimes nouns are the names of things that can't be seen or touched. This group (called ABSTRACT NOUNS) includes feelings (e.g. happiness), activities (e.g. sport) and studies (e.g. geometry). Some nouns are the names of groups or collections (e.g. swarm).

Do the cross-reference puzzle below.

To work out the answers, write the letter that corresponds to the number in the reference box. Six letters are given to you. You have to work the rest out by yourself. All the words are nouns that have something to do with school.

6	8	12	16	3	8	18		16		10	16	7	8	4	16	8		
		17		11		3					12							
		12		17		7	4	26		3	8	12	17	6	3			
		10		8		17				7			16			12		
	18	10	15	2	18	6		5		5	8	10	26		11			18
	11	18				18				6			17			6		
	1	2	2	26	10		8			16	2	9	15	12	10	10		
	1		2		1		4			18			6		12			
14	8	2	9	8	6	18	20		15	17	12	20	14	18	2	11	4	5
	18		13		11		8					18		5				
10		19	12		10	15	8	4						15				
16		7	9	3		12	16	3	12	17	26		15	7				
7		17	10	8		15	7				15	12	10	6	8			
10		9		10	15	8	17	17	7	4	14		7					
10		10			18						4							
2				10	6	11	5	8	4	6	10							
18		9	12	14	4	8	6		8									
10			17		18	8	12	5	7	4	14	1	2	2	26			
			11			6												
M₉	A₁₂	T₆	3	E₈	M₉	A₁₂	T₆	7	16	S₁₀		3	2	9	8	22	2	18	26

1	2	3	4	5	6 = T	7	8 = E	9 = M	10 = S	11	12 = A	13
14	15	16 = C	17	18	19	20	21	22	23	24	25	26

Circle the letters as they are used: Ⓐ B Ⓒ Ⓓ Ⓔ F G H I J K L Ⓜ N O P Q R Ⓢ Ⓣ U V W X Y Z

Singular and Plural

SINGULAR means one. PLURAL means more than one. Most nouns change when their plural form is used. Bruce and Alison have been on a lovely picnic in Four Leaf Clover Forest. So they would not get lost, they left a trail of tiny bits of rice with plural words written on them. They also sprinkled rice with singular words written on them to please the highly-educated birds that flap around the place. By colouring the plural bits, you will show Bruce and Alison their path home. You can move up and down. You can move to the right or left. You cannot move diagonally. Start at the centre picture.

Some words do not change their form in the plural. Many fish have the same form in singular and plural. e.g. fish .... fish   cod .... cod

mackerel .... mackerel   salmon .... salmon   tuna .... tuna

mullet .... mullet   sheep .... sheep   deer .... deer

person	geese	children	horses	mice	aeroplanes	table	chair
dwarfs	feet	elephant	highway	shed	classrooms	wolves	rabbit
toes	shoe	letter	train	book	cupboard	arrow	cats	leaves
roofs	afternoon	teacher	clock	pudding	vegetable	mother	tomatoes
sisters	elves	peas	envelope	cloud	tree	woman	uncle	potatoes
television set	pianos	frog	school	grandfather	oxen	teeth
grandmother	valleys	soap	tooth	playground	babies	pencil
picture	boy	knives	girl		shark	chairs	knee
sandwich	sun	pillows	picnic		foxes	tables	pig
seaweed	hand	heroes	cake		footpath	radio	bus
cow	spoonfuls	women	crow	river	forest	pedestrian	princess
pea	men	pumpkin	paper	beach	saucepan	fork	knife	spoon	mushroom
fly	passers-by	mouse	bottle	hospital	elbow	tongue	country	duck
ant	coins	turkey	goose	chicken	hen	shells	baskets	shelves
ear	thieves	chiefs	breakfast	bear	gardens	glass	saucers
monkey	boat	echoes	afternoon	goat	ankles	ball	cups	nose
dress	shoes	hands	polar bear	stick	oceans	hall	kangaroos
coat	fleas	wombat	machine	needle	socks	moon	elephants
star	cabbages	bees	flowers	cities	dreams	plum	mosquitoes

Start *Finish*

Bruce's mother left him this job list.
Please help.
Jobs: paint the house blue, the roof orange, the grass green, the path brown, and the sky pink.
Thanks
Love Mum.

Verbs

Cross-reference

Our language is made up of words. These words do various jobs.

Words that tell what someone or something does in a sentence are called VERBS.

Example: Bruce ran outside, saw Alison and jumped for joy.

Bruce did three things in the above sentence; he <u>ran</u>, <u>saw</u> and <u>jumped</u>. These three words are verbs.

Do the cross-reference puzzle below.

To work out the answers, write the letter that corresponds to the number in the reference box. Five letters are given to you. You have to work the rest out by yourself. All the words are verbs. Most are in the present tense (happening now, not in the past). Sixteen are in the past tense (they have happened in the past). *Colour the past tense verbs in the puzzle.* They all go across.

21 L	3 I	4 S	7 T	1	22 N		4		5	9	14		10	23	2	25	21	1	20
	9			4	9	25							9						
	4	1	1		24		4	16	23	9	7	16	17	1		20			4
10		7			1			23		20		1			3				7
23		17	1	9	23			4	9	3	20			16		24			2
9			16			1		25			4	5	2	18	1				5
6	2	26	10	17	7		1	8	5	21	9	3	22		2			4	
			1				5			16		1		18		20	3	20	
23	9	22				19	21	14		7		1			17	2	5		
	4		16			2		19	3	15	15	21	1				7		
	18		12	26	11	5	1	20			24		1				17		
11			23			1			4	9	7		4	9	14		23		
9	22	4	25	1	23	1	20				7			3			2		
23		3				7		21	1	9	5	7		19	21	2	25		
16	9	7	16	17		20	23	2	5				23			1			
17		4			23		26		4	7	2	2	20			9			
		25		5	3	22	16	17				7			10	23	1	25	
10		4	9	10		22		17	9	20			1			22		2	
1		21	2	2	18			24		21	3	16	18				23		
7	9	21	18			21	3	1	20			7		7	17	3	22	18	

1	2	3 I	4 S	5	6	7 T	8	9	10	11	12	13
14	15	16	17	18	19	20	21 L	22 N	23	24	25	26

Circle the letters as they are used: A B C D E F G H (I) J K (L) M (N) O P Q R (S)(T) U V W X Y Z

VERBS are words that tell what a person or thing does in a sentence. Verbs often change their form according to the time something is done. Things can be done in the past, present or future.

Example: Present - Rover <u>is barking</u> at the postman.
Past - Rover <u>barked</u> at the postman last Tuesday.
He <u>has barked</u> at him on a number of occasions.
Future - Rover <u>will bark</u> at the postman tomorrow.

Poor Jim! He pressed the wrong button in his time machine and ended up in the past. At first he liked it but now he would like to get back to the present. He can only do this by following a path of past tense verbs. Colour the path to help him get back to the present so he doesn't miss out on his evening meal (cabbage on toast). You can go up, down or across but not diagonally. Start at the centre picture.

Note: Verbs are often made up of more than one word. In such cases there is a <u>main verb</u> and a helper called an <u>auxiliary</u>.

Example: 'is barking'; barking = main verb, is = the auxiliary.

will run	slept	cleaned	sank	listened	looked	kissed	screamed
answer	told	swim	jump	play	will jump	is barking	eat	said
opened	climbed	ask	write	fly	listened	sang	drank	drew	went
called	is barking	worked	spoke	grew	sleep	is sleeping	snore
boiled	talk	stood	played	will talk	is talking	tell	will tell
studied	dance	smile	thought	carry	will carry	is carrying	drop
watched	is dropping	looked	is eating	hear	laughed	stood	sat
floated	speak	wave	ate	is watching	drove	eats	wrote
started	will speak	kicked	had	smiled	yelled	slide	talked
dropped	is jumping	reads	is reading	stop	will stop	walked
closed	followed	is scratching			ran	jumped	cried	swam
fold	lived	will answer			work	will work	is working
touch	invited	is touching			will swim	is swimming	buy
will go	used	will listen			is barking	will bark	kiss
lift	asked	make	is making	will make	is shopping	loose	will growl
sailed	answered	turn	will turn	is turning	will look	shouting	say
patted	is crying	will cry	is sitting	will laugh	go	chuckle	burn
replied	will smile	is smiling	think	hopped	coughed	remembering	see
showed	galloped	caught	destroyed	flew	finished	will ask	will use

Start (near "ran" / "jumped")

Finish (near bottom)

Select five verbs from above and put them into sentences.

_____

_____

_____

_____

Adjectives

We can make our writing more interesting by the use of adjectives. ADJECTIVES are the words used to describe people or things. By using them we give readers important information, we describe and add interest.

Example: boy   but ... handsome boy

charming boy

witty boy

intelligent boy

strong boy

Peter is a boy. What sort of boy is Peter? By using any or all of the adjectives listed to describe him, we give more information in our sentence and make it more interesting. (You are more interested in him now, aren't you?)

In the frames below, draw characters from any story or stories you have recently read.

Underneath each character list five suitable adjectives describing him or her. Don't use the same adjective twice. English is a wonderful language because there are many ways of saying the same thing. If characteristics are alike in some way, use <u>synonyms</u> (words with similar meanings).

Character: _____

Story: _____

Adjectives: _____

_____

_____

_____

Character: _____

Story: _____

Adjectives: _____

_____

_____

_____

Think of an adjective then draw it.

SCARY

The words related to the topic can be found in blocks in the puzzle. Words read letter to letter in any direction except diagonally. Every letter has been used. No letter is shared by words. One example is done. *Colour answer blocks that connect with one another different colours.*

E	V	E	R	Y	W	H	E	F	D	E	W
S	L	E	P	N	D	E	R	O	L	L	O
Y	E	S	T	U	W	O	R	K	E	D	P
R	E	T	W	O	U	N	D	E	C	A	E
D	A	Y	A	R	G	R	E	F	U	L	S
D	E	K	L	W	H	G	Y	T	O	L	A
D	A	I	L	Y	E	R	L	W	M	Y	E
H	A	P	P	F	R	E	I	O	O	**P**	S
R	L	Y	I	L	E	E	D	R	R	**L**	R
A	L	U	L	I	E	S	Y	L	**D**	**A**	E
R	E	G	Y	U	S	U	A	L	**E**	**Y**	V
B	E	A	U	T	I	F	U	L	L	Y	O

DAILY   REGULARLY
FLIES   YESTERDAY
<u>PLAYED</u>   FOLLOWED
SLEPT   TOMORROW
USUALLY   WORKED
HAPPILY   OVERSEAS
GREEDILY   WALKED
PEACEFULLY   WHERE
EVERYWHERE
UNDERGROUND
BEAUTIFULLY

ADVERBS are words that describe verbs. They do this in the three main ways shown below. *Use words from the list above to fill in the gaps.*

<u>Adverbs of manner</u> tell us <u>how</u> something is done.

Example: The children played happily.

What did they do? (the verb) _____

How did they do it? (the adverb) _____

        Brian slept peacefully.

What did he do? (the verb) _____

How did he do it? (the adverb) _____

<u>Adverbs of time</u> tell us <u>when</u> something is done.

Example: Jim usually flies to Spain for his holidays.

What does he do? (the verb) _____

When does he do it? (the adverb) _____

        Mary walked to school yesterday.

What did she do? (the verb) _____

When did she do it? (the adverb) _____

<u>Adverbs of place</u> tell us <u>where</u> something is done.

Example: Mice followed the Pied Piper everywhere.

What did they do? (the verb) _____

Where did they do it? (the adverb) _____

        The miners worked underground.

What did they do? (the verb) _____

Where did they do it? (the adverb) _____

Complete these sentences using words from the list. The word in brackets tells you the type of adverb to be used.

1. You should eat fruit
_____. (When)

2. We are going to London
_____. (When)

3. Jim is fit because he exercises
_____. (When)

4. Rover ate his food
_____.(How)

5. Alison sang
_____. (How)

6. _____ are my books? (Where)

7. My penfriend lives
_____. (Where)

Personal Pronouns

These words are PERSONAL PRONOUNS: I, me, mine, myself, my, you, yours, yourself, your, he, him, his, himself, she, her, herself, it, its, itself, we, us, ours, ourselves, our, yourselves, they, them, theirs, themselves, their.

Personal pronouns take the place of nouns in a sentence.

Without them our writing and speech would be very repetitive.

Example: Jim took out <u>his</u> lunchbox, opened <u>it</u> and began eating <u>his</u> lunch.

Without personal pronouns this would read as:

Jim took out <u>Jim's</u> lunchbox, opened <u>Jim's lunchbox</u> and began eating <u>Jim's</u> lunch.

Circle and then colour the pronouns in the sentences below. Rule lines from each dot to dot to make a picture.

1. I spy with my little eye something beginning with 'p'.
2. Me too!
3. Jason did his homework all by himself.
4. Mary was very happy when she saw her lamb.
5. 'You should be proud of yourselves!' said the headteacher to David and John.
6. 'They are very proud of themselves,' said their mothers.
7. 'Yes, we are proud of ourselves!' said David.
8. Our uncle came to visit us during the Christmas holidays.
9. What day is it?
10. He taught him to play the xylophone.
11. The kitten has lost its mittens.
12. The solitary wasp lives by itself.
13. Is that pen mine or yours?
14. 'Jack sold them your cow for a handful of beans,' said the farmer to Jack's mother.

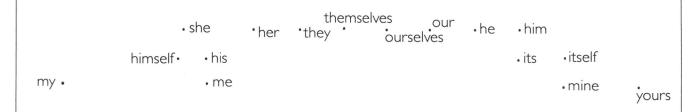

you•   •   •their •we   •us   •it
   yourselves

•she   •her •they •   •our   •he   •him
   themselves   ourselves

himself•   •his   •its   •itself

my •   •me   •mine
                                          yours

                              your•   •them

I

Colour all of the sections below according to the key.
Key: NOUNS ....blue, PRONOUNS ....yellow, ADJECTIVES.............green, VERBS .... orange, ADVERBS ....brown

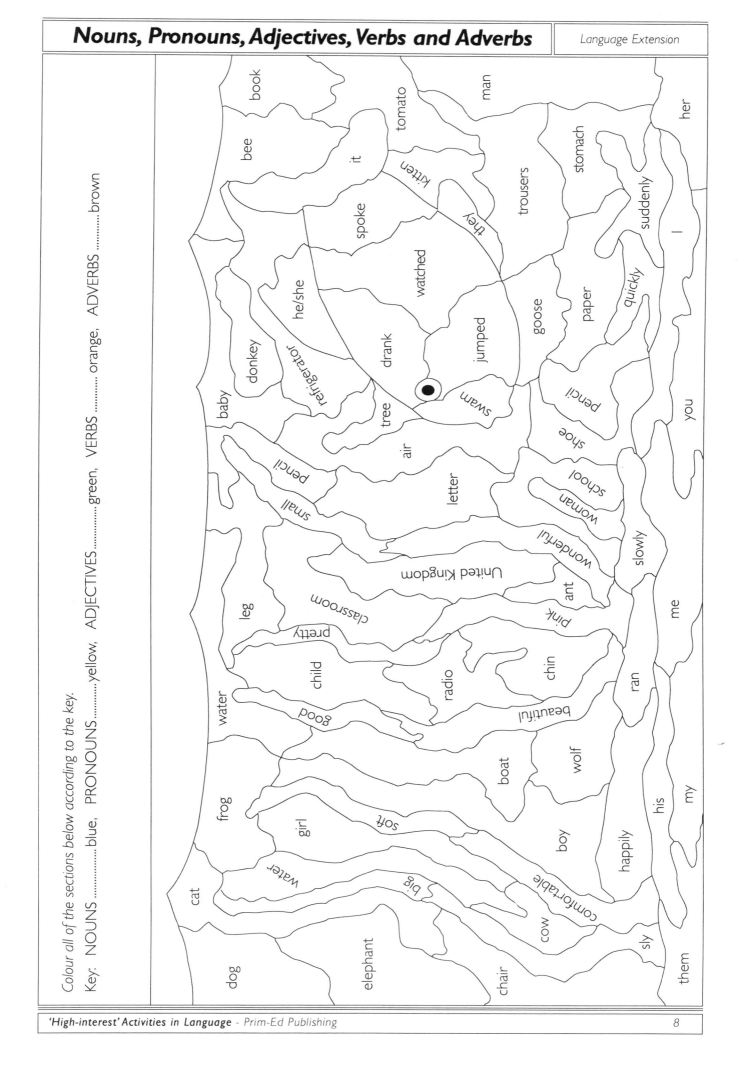

Prepositions

PREPOSITIONS are words that are placed in front of nouns or pronouns to show the relationship of the noun or pronoun to some other word in the sentence.

Example: A big brown dog sat <u>in</u> the kennel.

The preposition is <u>in</u>. It tells us where the dog was in relation to the kennel.
The dog was <u>in</u> the kennel, not <u>beside</u> it or <u>behind</u> it etc.
Listed are some common prepositions, use these to describe Paul's journey to work.
Colour the boxes of the preposition you use. The first letters are given to help you.

At about 6 a.m. Paul walks th_____ the door and goes do_____
                   1.   2.

the stairs. He then walks al_____ the garden path and tiptoes
                          3.

ac_____ a rickety old bridge. He walks ar_____
    4.   5.

Farmer Brown's field which has beehives i_____ it. Now he must go
                                6.

to_____ the Blue Hills until turning ne_____ Appleberry Road.
    7.   8.

He follows this road t_____ Candyfloss Forest. Sometimes he stops to
                      9.

rest un_____ a tree. After a short nap the serious work begins. This is
       10.

a windy place and he often must walk ag_____ the wind. If it is too windy he
                               11.

goes in_____ a secret tunnel that he has burrowed himself with his
        12.

teeth and claws. He walks be_____ ground level for one
                        13.

hundred metres passing un_____ the cottage of the three bears
                14.

and be_____ the thimble factory. When he emerges fr_____
        15.   16.

the tunnel he must cross the river ov_____ some stepping stones, then pass
                        17.

be_____ two giant oak trees. At last he arrives ready for work as chief
   18.

taster in a jam factory.

about
above
across
after
against
along
among
around
at
before
behind
below
beneath
beside
between
beyond
by
down
for
from
in
into
near
off
on
over
round
outside
inside
through
to
through
towards
under
underneath
up

Contractions

Sometimes, especially when speaking, words are shortened. An apostrophe is used to show where letters have been omitted from the second word when it was joined to the first.

The extended forms of words that are often contracted are listed below. Their contracted forms are written near the dots underneath the list. Following the list order, rule lines from dot to dot as you match the extended form to its contraction.

Write the contraction next to its extended form.

1.	are not	_____aren't_____
2.	was not	_____
3.	we will	_____
4.	do not	_____
5.	it will	_____
6.	we are	_____
7.	is not	_____
8.	will not	_____
9.	he is/has	_____
10.	who is/has	_____
11.	did not	_____
12.	I am	_____
13.	have not	_____
14.	it is/has	_____
15.	shall not	_____
16.	where is/has	_____
17.	must not	_____
18.	you will	_____
19.	there is/has	_____
20.	you have	_____
21.	could not	_____
22.	he will	_____
23.	we have	_____

24.	would not	_____
25.	she will	_____
26.	I have	_____
27.	would have	_____
28.	should not	_____
29.	could have	_____
30.	were not	_____
31.	you are	_____
32.	she is/has	_____
33.	that is/has	_____
34.	they have	_____
35.	does not	_____
36.	they are	_____
37.	cannot	_____
38.	I will	_____
39.	let us	_____
40.	had not	_____
41.	they will	_____
42.	what is	_____
43.	has not	_____
44.	should have	_____
45.	are not	_____

haven't ·   ·it's

·I'm   ·shan't   · wouldn't   ·she'll

didn't ·   ·where's   would've ·   ·I've

who's·   ·mustn't   ·couldn't

         you've

won't ·   ·you'll   ·he'll   ·shouldn't

   he's   there's   we've   could've

we're ·   ·isn't

it'll·   ·don't

wasn't ·   ·we'll

hasn't ·   ·what's   let's   ·I'll   doesn't ·they've   you're

                                                    weren't

·aren't   should've   they'll·   ·hadn't   can't·   ·they're   that's·   ·she's

Punctuation

There are a number of ways we can share our ideas with other people. The most common way is by talking. When we talk we do not need to worry about punctuation. When we write our ideas down, however, there are certain rules we must obey. Our ideas must be broken into units called sentences. You might think of sentences as descriptions of single things happening. Each sentence is a description of a single event taking place. In some sentences more than one thing can take place as long as a joining word (like 'and') is used to join the events.

Act out the sentences below.

The people and things in the following passages do many things (eg: cry, snore, buzz). Count how many different things the people or things do.

Finally, write the passage with correct punctuation.

Rapunzel

rapunzel sat in the tower she was crying a witch had locked her in there suddenly she heard a voice a handsome prince was calling her

Alison's Journey

alison boarded the train she sat in a seat the train began to move alison looked out the window she waved to grandmother the train began to move faster after a few minutes alison fell asleep she began snoring loudly mother woke her they both got off the train

Farm Life

peter lives on a farm he works hard he feeds the hens he collects the eggs his father drives the truck he milks the cows his mother looks after the house she cooks the meals

In some of the little stories below some of the sentences have more than one thing happening in them. This can only happen where a joining word is used. Act out the passages and decide how many sentences there are.

Stormy Weather

jim walked outside the wind was blowing rain began to fall lightning flashed jim ran inside and hid behind his hands

In the Countryside

bertie butterfly was sunning himself on a rock ronald rabbit hopped by and greeted him edward earwig peeked out from under a piece of bark dorothy dragonfly buzzed by the sun shone brightly curly the caterpillar crawled by all of the animals scurried to a safe place when the scent of man came into the field   (two joining words)

Characters: Rapunzel - Rapunzel, witch, a handsome prince
Alison's Journey - Alison, the train, Alison's mother
Farm Life - Peter, Father, Mother
Stormy Weather - Jim, wind, rain, lightning
In the Countryside - Bertie Butterfly, Ronald Rabbit, Edward Earwig, Dorothy Dragonfly, Curly the Caterpillar, the scent of a man.

Some words stand alone and some need auxiliaries (helpers).

Example: <u>drew</u> stands alone and <u>drawn</u> needs a helper. John <u>drew</u> a picture.
Andrew <u>has drawn</u> a picture. *Highlight the correct word in the sentences below then find the word in the puzzle and colour it the colour shown in brackets.*

1. Bruce (did/done) his homework. *(pink)*	2. I (saw/seen) a ghost last night. *(orange)*	3. Jim has (did/done) the dishes. *(red)*
4. I have just (saw/seen) Mary. *(blue)*	5. Peter has (sang/sung) before the King. *(brown)*	6. Anne (sang/sung) happily to herself. *(purple)*
7. Sally (drank/drunk) two jugs of goat's milk. *(green)*	8. Brooke has (drank/drunk) all of the lemonade. *(red)*	9. Daniel (swam/swum) across the pool. *(pink)*
10. Robert has (swam/swum) in his race. *(orange)*	11. Amanda has (ate/eaten) all of the chocolate. *(purple)*	12. The three little pigs (ate/eaten) a lot. *(blue)*
13. The children have (began/begun) their test. *(blue)*	14. Alison (began/begun) her story. *(pink)*	15. Jodie has (went/gone) to the pictures. *(orange)*
16. John (gone/went) fishing. *(purple)*	17. 'I have (broke/broken) my pencil,' wailed Karl. *(pink)*	18. Kate (broke/broken) three eggs. *(purple)*
19. That bird has (flew/flown) all the way from China. *(blue)*	20. Superman (flew/flown) to the scene of the crime. *(brown)*	21. Karen has (shook/shaken) the hand of Cockatoo Clarrie, the famous pop singer. *(blue)*
22. The buildings (shook/shaken) during the earthquake. *(orange)*	23. Paul has (forgotten/forgot) his books. *(green)*	24. Erica (forgot/forgotten) her lunch. *(brown)*
25. Bob has just (wrote/written) a beautiful poem about slugs. *(green)*	26. Lisa (wrote/written) a very long book about string. *(brown)*	27. Melanie (ran/run) to the sweet shop. *(brown)*
28. I have (ran/run) all the way home, from my school. *(purple)*	29. 'I have (spoken/spoke),' said the chief, wisely. *(brown)*	30. Nikki (spoke/spoken) to the teacher. *(green)*
31. Donna has (rang/rung). *(brown)*	32. I (rang/rung) my friend, Tracy. *(brown)*	33. Stuart has (fell/fallen) out of many trees when climbing. *(green)*
34. A star (fallen/fell) from heaven. *(pink)*		

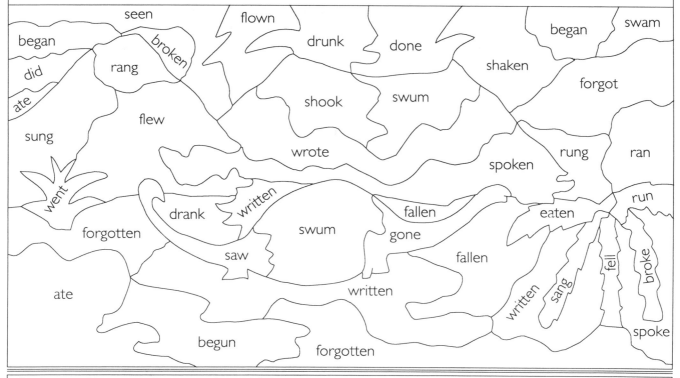

Spoonerisms

The English clergyman, W A Spooner, who was a college warden at Oxford University, was known to unintentionally transpose the beginnings of words with some humorous results. From his slips came a name for such mistakes: 'SPOONERISMS'.

Match the spoonerised words below, then write the correct word on the line provided.

Around the House

gack	boom	
wish	barden	__BACKGARDEN__
rining	lupboard	_____
par	dasher	_____
rath	kink	__KITCHEN SINK__
sitchen	doom	__DINING ROOM__
toof	cort	_____
cinen	boor	_____
dack	riles	_____

At the Beach

sife	sunes	_____
teach	rools	_____
burf	lavers	_____
cathing	hide	_____
gea	bowel	_____
tigh	bostumes	_____
dand	sulls	_____
bun	soard	_____
pock	sathers	_____

The Circus and Fair

salloon	shing	_____
tion	roaster	_____
thost	grain	_____
coller	bellers	_____
soconut	lamer	_____
tig	bop	_____
row	chy	_____
daw	feel	_____
wherris	sust	_____

Animals

dull	coach	_____
dein	quee	_____
mer	shog	_____
prench	lird	_____
deep	bog	_____
com	reer	_____
been	tat	_____
bady	foodle	_____
rock	tite	_____

At School

glay	skope	_____
cencil	pround	_____
baths	tooks	_____
bext	ceen	_____
ripping	pase	_____
balk	mook	_____
chool	mables	_____
tan	schild	_____
tultiplication	choard	_____

Famous People

Darles	Slimsoll	_____
Norence	Jennon	_____
Pamuel	Matcher	_____
Lohn	Chickens	_____
Thargaret	Dader	_____
Bord	Mandhi	_____
Bouglas	la Dinci	_____
Gahatma	Flightingale	_____
Veonardo	Laden-Powel	_____

Draw these 'city' spoonerisms:

laffic trights	poot fath	stus bop	leon nights	caxi tab

Match these spoonerised beginnings and endings, then write the completed word or words in the space provided.

Sports

lugby	lump	_____
mad	shumping	_____
tawn	binton	BADMINTON
bolley	reague	_____
jow	trump	_____
benpin	lennis	_____
jong	vall	_____
pot	towling	_____
jiple	shut	_____

Towns and Cities in the United Kingdom

hirming	morough	_____
biddles	karnock	_____
mil	hax	_____
fali	dam	_____
lunder	bam	_____
fel	bast	_____
tris	shury	_____
hur	bol	_____
brews	sand	_____
wor	sampton	_____
hotting	wester	_____
hipping	ciff	_____
dar	mock	_____
lat	cidge	_____
chin	chorton	_____
blaston	nam	_____
aouth	gury	_____
ramb	nich	_____

Capital Cities from around the World

don	cagen	_____
ban	hinki	_____
rad	nelhi	_____
hopen	mid	_____
sel	lon	_____
kang	lon	_____
dagh	bok	_____
dew	cerra	_____
bis	bad	_____

Famous Landmarks and Places

flack	balace	_____
hone	hall	_____
cuez	mintyre	_____
wadrian's	listrict	_____
nen	lidge	_____
cindsor	webbey	_____
flapa	sanal	_____
cuckingham	borest	_____
brondon	clover	_____
kull of	wastle	_____
sqrafalgar	tuare	_____
diffs of	bevis	_____
astminster	stenge	_____
dake	scow	_____

Characters from Fiction Stories

stumpel	praming	_____
boddy and	riltskin	_____
bleeping	nigears	_____
thom	thears	_____
bree	seauty	_____
ming	snite	_____
bin	kidas	_____
buss in	sad	_____
chince	poots	_____
whow	tumb	_____

Analogies

An ANALOGY is a comparison. It shows how things from different categories are similiar.

<u>Food</u> is to <u>person</u> as <u>petrol</u> is to <u>car</u>.

Food provides a person's energy and petrol is a car's source of energy.

Complete the analogies below by putting in a suitable word.

1. An Inuit person(eskimo) is to igloo as _____ is to hive.
2. Lava is to volcano as _____ is to hose.
3. Stripes are to zebra as _____ are to ladybird.
4. Roof is to house as _____ is to head.
5. Beak is to magpie as _____ is to duck.
6. Superman is to Metropolis as _____ is to Gotham City.
7. Steering wheel is to car as rudder is to _____.
8. Black Beauty is to horse as Moby Dick is to _____.
9. Eating fatty food is to heart disease as _____ is to lung cancer.
10. Bracelet is to wrist as ring is to _____.
11. Ferry is to water as train is to _____.
12. Broomstick is to witch as _____ is to astronaut.
13. Cow is to milk as _____ is to wool.
14. Dodo is to Mauritius as Emu is to _____.
15. Pip is to orange as _____ is to egg.
16. Fish is to aquarium as _____ is to library.
17. Farmer's wife is to Three Blind Mice as _____ is to Three Little Pigs.
18. Training is to athlete as homework is to _____.
19. Llama is to mountains as frog is to _____.
20. Rover is to dog as Dobbin is to _____.
21. Pied Piper is to Hamelin as Dick Whittington is to _____.
22. Rembrandt is to painting as Mozart is to _____.
23. Harbour Bridge is to Sydney as Eiffel Tower is to _____.
24. Tie is to neck as _____ is to flagpole.
25. Stop is to red as go is to _____
26. Horns are to bull as _____ are to elephant.
27. Buy is to bought as bring is to _____.
28. Lion tamer is to circus as teacher is to _____.
29. Oil is to well as coal is to _____.
30. Fur is to bear as _____ are to fish.
31. Ten is to toes as _____ is to ears.
32. Sand is to hourglass as _____ is to balloon.
33. King is to Queen as Prince is to _____.
34. Iceberg is to *Titanic* as Delilah is to _____.
35. Last is to first as _____ is to white.

Similes

The words related to the topic can be found in blocks in the puzzle. Words read letter to letter in any direction except diagonally. Every letter has been used. No letter is shared by words. One example is done. *Colour answer blocks that connect with one another different colours.*

A SIMILE is a figure of speech. It is used to express a resemblance in some form of one thing to another.

C	H	T	H	E	T	U	R	E	E	R
S	U	O	E	S	C	H	A	T	T	P
O	R	M	R	U	I	R	M	U	L	A
L	C	H	M	O	P	E	O	L	E	N
O	M	O	N	W	A	T	W	E	J	C
D	I	T	C	H	F	G	L	E	O	A
M	G	M	S	N	O	O	O	X	B	K
E	H	O	W	A	X	D	S	I	N	E
T	O	U	S	B	E	E	G	I	P	P
H	S	T	E	H	I	L	B	A	T	U
U	S	E	L	A	H	L	S	H	C	N

CHURCHMOUSE
DITCHWATER   BAT
METHUSELAH   DOG
MOTHER   PICTURE
PANCAKE   PUNCH
SOLOMON   OX
SWAN   MULE
BEE   HILLS
FOX   MOUSE
PIG   EEL
JOB   OWL
HATTER   SIN
GHOST

Complete the commonly used similes below, using words from the list.

1. As sick as a _____.
2. As poor as a <u>churchmouse</u>.
3. As blind as a _____.
4. As dull as _____.
5. As white as a _____.
6. As old as _____.
7. As old as the _____.
8. As flat as a _____.
9. As strong as an _____.
10. As devoted as a _____.
11. As busy as a _____.
12. As mad as a _____.
13. As sly as a _____.
14. As wise as _____ ___.
15. As wise as an _____.
16. As pleased as _____.
17. As fat as a _____.
18. As graceful as a _____.
19. As patient as _____.
20. As quiet as a _____.
21. As slippery as an _____.
22. As pretty as a _____.
23. As ugly as _____.
24. As stubborn as a _____.

Make up some of your own similes.

As hairy as _____.

As hot as _____.

As _____.

As _____.

As _____.

As _____.

The words related to the topic can be found in blocks in the puzzle. Words read letter to letter in any direction except diagonally. Every letter has been used. No letter is shared by words. One example is done. *Colour answer blocks that connect one another different colours.*

S	E	S	W	O	R	S	O	U	N	D	S
A	I	H	I	P	K	T	H	B	E	L	I
U	L	F	N	A	M	O	R	I	N	S	E
C	E	L	L	S	D	S	B	R	C	N	E
K	C	O	E	I	R	E	A	D	E	K	W
V	E	S	S	B	N	G	R	L	E	A	O
A	C	O	O	K	I	Y	L	W	A	T	R
S	R	D	F	S	W	B	D	T	R	E	M
O	A	A	E	R	O	I	R	R	U	T	H
R	E	S	O	R	E	H	D	S	O	T	D
R	H	T	B	A	N	G	E	L	O	Y	R
O	W	I	N	G	O	U	B	**B**	**U**	**S**	**H**

A'SORROWING BED
WORKMAN DRY
EARLY BIRD LIE
A'BORROWING BIRDS
HEARD LEAK
SILENCE BIRD
SAUCE FEAST
COOKS WORM
VESSELS BROTH
ENOUGH SHIP
FLOCK SEEN
SOUND TOOLS
WATER TRUTH
BUSH

A PROVERB is a wise saying that is intended to teach us something. Proverbs are often used to briefly state the lesson taught to us in such stories as fables. *Use the correct words from the list to complete these proverbs, the first letter of each word has been given to help you.*

1. A small l_____ will sink a great s_____.

2. S_____ gives consent.

3. B_____ of a feather f_____ together.

4. Empty v_____ make the most s_____.

5. Too many c_____ spoil the b_____.

6. A b_____ in the hand is worth two in the <u> bush </u>.

7. E_____ is as good as a f_____.

8. We never miss the w_____ till the well runs d_____.

9. A bad w_____ always blames his t_____.

10. Hunger is the best s_____.

11. Little children should be s_____ and not h_____.

12. T_____will out.

13. The e_____ catches the w_____.

14. As you make your b_____ so must you l_____ in it.

15. He goes a'_____ who goes a'_____.

Which proverbs apply to these kinds of people? (Write the numbers from the above proverbs.)

1. A silly person who is always talking about nothing of real importance. _____

2. Someone who is a very fussy eater. _____

3. A cricketer who blames his bat when he gets out. _____

Anagrams

The words in each example below are ANAGRAMS. Each word in the example has exactly the same letters but they are arranged in a different order. The first one is done for you. *Do the rest using the clues given to you.*

1. ECAH — every - <u>each</u>   pain - <u>ache</u>

2. UGM — chewing _____   drinking cup - _____

3. UCMH — a lot - _____   friend - _____

4. NWO — came first - _____   straight away - ___ _____
   possess - _____

5. ITPS — saliva - _____   trenches - _____
   touches lightly - _____

6. EPLES — orange skins - _____   slumber - _____

7. EPST — nuisance - _____   part of a staircase - _____
   tame animal friends - _____

8. ALSI — part of a yacht - _____   girl's name - _____
   another girl's name - _____   troubles - _____

9. NUAT — type of fish - _____
   type of seed (two words) - _____
   your mother or father's sister - _____

10. ALEF — annoying insect - _____   part of a tree - _____

11. DHASE — one side of a coin - _____   shelter from the sun - _____
    extra building in some people's back gardens (two words)- _____

12. APSNI — aches - _____   a country in Europe - _____

13. AKSO — trees - _____   to drench - _____

14. EOHS — garden tools - _____   footwear - _____
    you use it to water the garden - _____

15. ETNS — column between the units and hundreds - _____
    a bird's home - _____
    used by people to catch fish - _____
    dispatched - _____

16. EARWDR — person who guards prisoners - _____
    part of a cupboard or chest - _____
    special payment offered for information - _____

17. ETMAS — calms down - _____   sporting groups - _____
    friends - _____   pork, steak etc. - _____
    water vapour - _____

18. ATDRE — to swap - _____   ranked - _____
    gripping pattern on a tyre - _____

19. ASECP — steps - _____   this is all around you - _____
    clothing worn mostly by superheroes - _____

20. ANDW — daybreak - _____   magic stick - _____

Tautology

TAUTOLOGY is the needless repetition of an idea in a sentence.

Example: On _rainy_ _wet_ nights I like to lie in bed and read a book.

Underline or highlight the unnecessary word or words in the sentences below.

1. 'That song was recorded at a concert by Elvis Presley in 1960 while he was still alive,' said the radio announcer.

2. Me, myself, personally, I don't look good in pink.

3. 'I did not hear you the first time, Mr Prime Minister, so would you repeat that again,' said the journalist.

4. The frozen ice soon melted in Lisa's lunchbox.

5. That often happens to me regularly.

6. It has never happened to me, ever.

7. 'The suspect is bald, has beady eyes, no hair and is of a dirty appearance,' said the newsreader.

8. One bite from that huge tropical insect crawling up your collar could kill a person stone dead.

9. The children were filthy dirty after playing in the mud.

10. The sky was clear and cloudless on Friday morning.

11. The koala is a very unique Australian animal.

12. The front row forward scored a try over the opposition's goal line.

13. 'The price of things is always increasing more and more,' said the angry shopper.

14. The explorers descended down into the cave.

15. Zelda got all of the calculations completely wrong.

16. Is that story really true?

17. Jim's birthday day is on the thirteenth of April.

18. Bruce didn't have one single penny in his piggy bank.

19. The thumb on my hand is sore.

20. 'Advance forward!' shrieked the excited coach to his players.

21. 'Two eggs will be adequate enough,' said the customer to the waiter.

22. A big giant stood in the doorway.

23. 'You are beautifully pretty,' said Bill, making Alison blush.

24. One morning before noon there was a loud knock at Terry's front door.

25. The batsman was bowled for a duck before scoring any runs.

26. 'Children who tell untrue lies will be punished,' said the headteacher fiercely.

27. I always tell the truth every time.

28. The old sailor told tales of the many distant faraway lands he had visited.

29. In some cities smog levels become dangerously unsafe.

30. In cold weather my big toe gets painfully sore.

31. Clarence the Cork escaped by floating on the stream on top of the water.

32. 'Biscuits and cookies are my favourite foods,' drooled Noel.

Now you, yourself, personally make up some of your own tautologies by yourself.

_____

_____

Compound Words

In each group below a single word can be added to the beginning to form new compound words or commonly used word combinations. If you are uncertain of a word, use your dictionary to check.

Example: f i n g e r   nail
print
tips

1. ___ ___ ___

tune
ward
get

2. ___ ___ ___ ___

ache
light
master

3. ___ ___ ___ ___ ___

board
beaten
forecast

4. ___ ___ ___

cap
house
man

5. ___ ___ ___ ___

coat
come
balance

6. ___ ___ ___ ___ ___

works
wool
guitar

7. ___ ___ ___ ___

powder
sitter
face

8. ___ ___ ___ ___

thing
body
where

9. ___ ___ ___ ___

dog
spur
water bottle

10. ___ ___ ___ ___ ___

house
land
belt

11. ___ ___ ___

screen
break
mill

12. ___ ___ ___ ___

mat
bell
knob

13. ___ ___ ___ ___

flake
board
man

14. ___ ___ ___ ___

spread
eyed
awake

15. ___ ___ ___ ___ ___

hair
radish
power

16. ___ ___ ___ ___ ___

ordinary
sensory
terrestrial

17. ___ ___ ___

case
hatch
cracker

18. ___ ___ ___ ___

card
code
office

19. ___ ___ ___ ___ ___

yard
mouse
service

20. ___ ___ ___ ___

war
servant
engineer

21. ___ ___ ___ ___

stairs
hearted
trodden

22. ___ ___ ___ ___

house
paper
blower

23. ___ ___ ___ ___

vault
cat
axe

24. ___ ___ ___ ___ ___

screen
stack
bomb

25. ___ ___ ___

lark
scraper
high

26. ___ ___ ___ ___

wire
seed
stack

27. ___ ___ ___ ___

mate
yard
wreck

28. ___ ___ ___ ___ ___

fall
front
pistol

29. ___ ___ ___ ___

setter
shaker
meal

30. ___ ___ ___ ___ ___ ___

Smith
flat
knot

Well-known Opposites

If you replace each word below with its opposite you will form some well-known terms.
Example: scarce hot = <u>c</u> <u>o</u> <u>m</u> <u>m</u> <u>o</u> <u>n</u>   <u>c</u> <u>o</u> <u>l</u> <u>d</u>. Each space stands for a letter.
The word meanings are given.

1.   white ugliness = the name of a well known book about a horse.

    __ __ __ __ __   __ __ __ __ __ __

2.   death spender = someone who watches over swimmers on the beach.

    __ __ __ __   __ __ __ __ __

3.   over sit = to comprehend the meaning

    __ __ __ __ __ __ __ __ __ __

4.   in front = Australia's remote bush country

    __ __ __ __ __ __ __ __

5.   low dark = the most exciting or memorable part

    __ __ __ __ __ __ __ __ __

6.   right under = the unused portion of food or material

    __ __ __ __ __ __ __ __ __

7.   arm start = a popular story from olden times

    __ __ __ __ __ __

8.   foot you up = a secondhand piece of clothing

    __ __ __ __ - __ __ - __ __ __ __

9.   out go = money received for work etc.

    __ __ __ __ __ __

10.   standing cow = an American Indian chief who led the Sioux Indians in the 1870s

    __ __ __ __ __ __ __   __ __ __ __

11.   fix slow = a meal eaten at the beginning of the day

    __ __ __ __ __ __ __ __ __

12.   empty front = a position in football

    __ __ __ __ __ __ __ __ __

13.   square down = the driving together of cattle to get them ready for branding or market etc.

    __ __ __ __ __ - __ __

14.   take out = to admit defeat, surrender

    __ __ __ __   __ __

15.   foot sit = a gymnastics activity/skill

    __ __ __ __ __ __ __ __ __

16.   bad night = a common greeting or farewell

    __ __ __ __   __ __ __ __

17.   rise in = radioactive material caused by a nuclear explosion

    __ __ __ __ __ __ __

18.   thin him = a member of the family

    __ __ __ __ __ __

19.   day stallion = an unpleasant dream

    __ __ __ __ __ __ __ __

20.   big men = name of a well known book by Lousia May Alcott

    __ __ __ __ __ __   __ __ __ __

Make up some of your own.

_____

_____

_____

The words related to the topic can be found in blocks in the puzzle. Words read letter to letter in any direction except diagonally. Every letter has been used. No letter is shared by words. One example has been done for you. *Colour answer blocks that connect one another different colours. Find the words you have made in the sentences below in the building block puzzle.*

D	A	O	N	E	S	T	C	I	P	S	A
C	B	H	F	I	R	E	A	D	U	T	I
H	I	P	A	N	K	L	I	M	O	A	L
K	C	O	C	O	I	N	N	A	T	R	T
X	Y	L	N	S	K	K	L	E	P	U	S
A	T	U	A	T	R	E	H	D	B	A	T
F	U	L	T	U	M	E	G	E	U	R	S
G	V	A	S	E	L	A	P	N	N	N	D
H	A	N	I	G	M	S	P	E	M	E	K
B	L	E	T	A	U	T	O	T	U	F	C
A	H	O	S	C	D	E	N	U	D	E	A
T	G	R	I	B	T	N	U	A	H	I	J

The missing letters from the words below are consecutive in the alphabet. *Complete the words by putting in the missing consecutive letters.*

A B C D E F G H I
J K L M N O P Q R
S T U V W X Y Z

1. a small water bird - d <u>a</u> <u>b</u> <u>c</u> hick.
2. a piece of kitchen furniture - t ___ ___ le.
3. to take over a vehicle like a truck or lorry by force - ___ ___ ___ ack.
4. a spirit - ___ ___ ost.
5. part of the skeleton - ri ___ ___ age.
6. the opposite of attack - ___ ___ ___ end.
7. a season - autu ___ ___.
8. silly - ___ ___ ___ pid.
9. where the winner finishes - fi ___ ___ ___.
10. part of the body - an ___ ___ e.
11. clothing worn by actors - co ___ ___ ___ me.
12. a musical instrument made up of wooden bars - ___ ___ l ___ ___ hone.
13. the country that borders Pakistan's north - A ___ ___ ___ ani ___ ___ an.
14. closed - u ___ ___ ___ ened.
15. part of the hand - pa ___ ___.
16. you are one - ___ ___ ___ dent.
17. a country - Au ___ ___ ralia.
18. a group of nine small islands in the Pacific Ocean - ___ ___ ___ alu.
19. a small cucumber often used in pickles - ___ ___ erkin.
20. what an over-inflated balloon will do - bu ___ ___ ___.
21. a person with an irresistible desire to steal - ___ ___ eptomaniac.

The gaps below can be filled with a single letter of the alphabet. Each letter is used once only. *Cross off the letters from the alphabet list below as you use them.*

A   B   C   D   E   F   G   H   I   J   K   L   M   N   O   ~~P~~   Q   R   S   T   U   V   W   X   Y   Z

1.   Bruce ate three large bowls of __P__ soup.

2.   'Not another matching tie and sock set,' thought Superman, looking at the carefully wrapped birthday present with his _____-ray vision.

3.   Has anyone ever found out _____ the chicken crossed the road?

4.   There was a long _____ lining up for tickets at the football match.

5.   'Act your _____ Darren, you big baby!' roared the teacher.

6.   'Who'_____ that?' asked Jim trying to look surprised yet fierce.

7.   'That bird is a blue _____,' said the park ranger.

8.   '_____ too can have a body like mine,' said the muscleman in the advertisement.

9.   '_____ dear, I've locked my keys inside,' sighed Mary.

10.   'You will now write a five page _____ay about string,' said the teacher.

11.   Rembrandt was a famous _____tist.

12.   '_____ up!' said the cowboy to his horse.

13.   When you finish doing this exercise, go and have a cup of _____.

14.   Fred often eats at the _____ty Tummy Restaurant.

15.   The Allied invasion of Europe in 1944 took place on a day codenamed _____ Day.

16.   With great _____ort June clambered up the staircase.

17.   Lisa looks even more beautiful in her new _____ glasses.

18.   The world's second highest mountain is called _____ 2 or Mount Godwin Austen.

19.   'I can _____ with my duplicating machine,' laughed the mad scientist.

20.   Our classroom is like a _____ hive of activity.

21.   Does she really sell _____ shells by the seashore?

22.   'Don't be fooled by its appearance. This car is in _____ one condition,' said the salesman with an unconvincing smile.

23.   _____ster Island in the Pacific Ocean is best known for the gigantic stone figures made by its ancient inhabitants.

24.   When a driver is learning to drive, the car must display _____ plates.

25.   Hippies hold up two fingers in a _____ shape to symbolise peace.

26.   I suppose this must be the _____d.

Which letters make the sounds that give the words to fit the clues below? The numbers of letters you need is given in brackets.

horse (2) _____   not full (2) _____   'yes' in the navy (2) _____

US soldier (2) _____   plural of 'is' (1) _____   all correct (2) _____

person who plays records at a disco (2) _____

Tony has joined Robin Hood's merry band. One day as he loafed idly in the forest an arrow whizzed past his nose and thudded into a nearby tree. Tied to it was a strange message. On the back were written the directions you see written below. *Follow the directions and you will see why Tony zoomed away with winged feet.*

Message: **KB GNKMOC BHYLKFF WHY!**

1.   Move WHY to the front.

   _____

2.   Change the Ws to Ts.

   _____

3.   Move the last word into the second position.

   _____

4.   Change the Ys to Es.

   _____

5.   The Bs are really Ss, change them around.

   _____

6.   L stands for R. Change it.

   _____

7.   Rewrite the last word reversing the spelling.

   _____

8.   Change the Ks into Is and write the message.

   _____

As Tony sped through the forest, another arrow flew past him and thunked into another tree. On it was another strange message with directions on the back. The paper bore the Sheriff of Nottingham's letterhead. *Follow the directions to work out the Sheriff's message.*

Message: **ETSNW EM'IW ESNW!**

1.   Put the first word at the end of the message.

   _____

2.   Swap the positions of the first and second words.

   _____

3.   Leave out all the Es.

   _____

4.   Change all the Ss into Os.

   _____

5.   Leave out all the Ws.

   _____

6.   Reverse the spelling of all the words.

   _____

Worm Words

Most big words are made up of smaller words or sounds called syllables. Link the syllables below so that each worm makes a word. Make worms in each group different colours from one another.

Write the complete word formed on the line near the worm's head.

A.   These worm words are all ways of <u>speaking</u>.

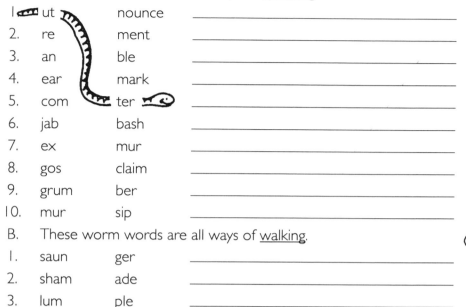

1.   ut   nounce   _____
2.   re   ment   _____
3.   an   ble   _____
4.   ear   mark   _____
5.   com   ter   _____
6.   jab   bash   _____
7.   ex   mur   _____
8.   gos   claim   _____
9.   grum   ber   _____
10. mur   sip   _____

B.   These worm words are all ways of <u>walking</u>.

1.   saun   ger   _____
2.   sham   ade   _____
3.   lum   ple   _____
4.   tram   ble   _____
5.   stag   ter   _____
6.   par   ber   _____

C.   These worm words are longer and they can be used to mean <u>bad</u>.

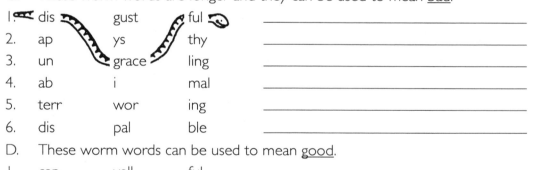

1.   dis   gust   ful   _____
2.   ap   ys   thy   _____
3.   un   grace   ling   _____
4.   ab   i   mal   _____
5.   terr   wor   ing   _____
6.   dis   pal   ble   _____

D.   These worm words can be used to mean <u>good</u>.

1.   cap   vell   ful   _____
2.   won   i   ent   _____
3.   ex   stand   ous   _____
4.   out   der   ing   _____
5.   ex   quis   tal   _____
6.   mar   cell   ite   _____

Make up some of your own worm words in one of these categories: boys' names; girls' names; things at your school.

1.   _____   _____   _____   _____
2.   _____   _____   _____   _____
3.   _____   _____   _____   _____
4.   _____   _____   _____   _____
5.   _____   _____   _____   _____

Bruce is a bookworm. At the moment his other craze is worms. Most especially, he is interested in **earthworms**. Sometimes, nasty people would try to upset him by calling him a worm. Nowadays he takes this as a compliment. He is reading about worms. Bruce is building a respect for the worm for the very important part it plays in the pattern of nature.

Before learning so much about them, Bruce looked on worms as being fairly uncomplicated fellows. Now he knows better. In fact, they aren't fellows at all.

Worms live in burrows in the ground.
Farmers and gardeners love them. They know that worms are great enrichers of the soil.
Their burrows break up the soil, loosening it and letting in air.

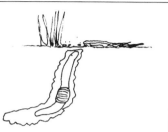

Worms eat decayed plant matter. They emerge at night, taking their food back inside the burrow with them to enjoy at their leisure.

Worms do not have eyes but do have organs that are sensitive to light.

Worms' bodies are made up of segments. There are usually about 160 of these. They are stretched and then contracted when the worm moves.
A grip is kept on the ground or sides of the worm's burrow with spiny outgrowths called chaetae.

A **worm** will eat and cast its own weight every 24 hours.
If you have a kilogram of worms in a patch of soil, that's a kilo of fertiliser being put into the soil every 24 hours.
This is far better for the soil than adding artificial chemical fertilisers.

Worms belong to a group of animals known as hermaphrodites (when broken into syllables: *herm/aph/ro/dites*). This means each worm has both male and female parts.

Worms are capable of both producing eggs and fertilising the eggs of other worms.
This is what happens when earthworms pair.
So each worm is the mother of worms produced from its own eggs and the father of worms produced by another worm.

Young worms develop in cocoons left in the soil by the parent worm.

saddle

Moving left on this page the worm does the following: the chaetae behind the part of the worm's body called the saddle hold onto the soil and the front part of the body stretches forward; the chaetae in the front section hold onto the soil while those at the back are pulled out.
The front section contracts to normal size pulling the rear part forward. The thickened part of the worm's body commonly called the saddle or clitellum is where cocoons for **young worms** are produced.

Bruce has decided to make a little compost heap for his new pets. He will use a container with some form of cover but no bottom and with holes in the sides.

Inside he is going to put layers of soil and plant scraps.
He will place a handful of **worms** in the top, put on the cover and visit it regularly to see what takes place.
On some of his visits he will drop some grass cuttings and leaves and see what becomes of them after a few days.
He will water it lightly and often enough to keep it moist but never too damp.

You could do this too and learn more about these interesting, helpful creatures.

Earthworms - Worksheet

A. *Write short answers to the questions below.*

1. Where do worms live? _____

2. How long does it take a worm to eat and cast its own weight? _____

3. What do worms eat? _____

4. When do worms usually come out? _____

5. What is the name of the animal group whose members have both male and female parts in each animal? _____

6. What are worms' bodies made up of? _____

7. What are the spiny outgrowths that act as their feet? _____

8. Give two names for the thickened part of the worm's body. _____

9. What are produced in this part? _____

10. What is Bruce building for his pet worms? _____

B. *Find the words with these meanings on the Fact Sheet. The first letter is given.*

1. Home for worms: w_____

2. Soil-enriching substance: f_____

3. Not natural: a_____

4. Free time: l_____

5. Simple: u_____

6. Making: p_____

7. Squeezed or brought together: c_____

8. Part: s_____

9. Often: r_____

10. Animals: c_____

C. *List:*

1. Two types of people that love worms: _____

2. Three things you could use to build a good compost heap for worms in your backyard:

    _____

D. *Skimming over the Fact Sheet, locate these words and write them in their order of appearance:*
   leisure, usually, nowadays, burrows, cast

    _____

E. *Answer the questions below in sentences.*

1. When and where do worms normally eat? _____

    _____

    _____

2. What are produced in the clitellum? _____

    _____

    _____

F. *Using the letters in* E A R T H W O R M, *make ten words of three letters or more. Use the letters only as often as they appear in 'earthworm'. Do not include people's names.*

    _____

    _____

G. *Research and creative writing: Pretend you are an earthworm. Write a story telling us about your life.*

Words in Words

Mark has a problem. When he opened his book, *The Baby Word Book*, many of the small words escaped and hid themselves in the bigger words of his spelling lists that he keeps on his wall. He knows exactly which words are missing and has left spaces for you to write them. For some tricky words he has even included a meaning. Please help.

Example: these tiny words were found by Mark hiding in 'classroom'.

CLASSROOM   <u>c l a s s</u>   <u>r o o m</u>   <u>l a s s</u>   <u>a s s</u>   <u>a s</u>

1. SUNSHINE   ___ ___ ___   ___ ___ ___ ___   ___ ___ ___ ___

    ___ ___ ___   ___ ___

2. CHILLY   ___ ___ ___ ___   ___ ___ ___ ___

    ___ ___ ___   ___ ___ ___ ___

3. DRAGONFLY   ___ ___ ___ ___ ___ ___   ___ ___ ___

    ___ ___ ___   ___ ___ ___   ___ ___ ___ ___

4. NEWSPAPER   ___ ___ ___   ___ ___ ___ ___   ___ ___ ___ ___

    ___ ___ ___ (mineral spring)   ___ ___ ___ (for every - e.g. mph)

5. FATHER   ___ ___ ___ ___   ___ ___ ___   ___ ___ ___

    ___ ___

6. SCREWDRIVER   ___ ___ ___ ___ ___   ___ ___ ___ ___ ___

    ___ ___ ___ ___   ___ ___ ___ ___ ___   ___ ___ ___ ___

7. EVERYTHING   ___ ___ ___ ___   ___ ___ ___ ___   ___ ___ ___ ___

    ___ ___ ___ ___ ___   ___ ___ ___   ___ ___ ___ ___ ___

    ___ ___ ___ (Adam's wife)

8. OVERFLOWING ___ ___ ___ ___   ___ ___ ___ ___   ___ ___ ___ ___

    ___ ___ ___ ___ ___ ___ ___ ___   ___ ___ ___ ___ ___   ___ ___ ___

    ___ ___ ___ ___ ___   ___ ___ ___ ___ ___ ___

    ___ ___ ___ ___   ___ ___ ___ ___ ___ ___ (when they moo cows are doing this)

9. FORGETTING   ___ ___ ___ ___ ___   ___ ___ ___ ___   ___ ___ ___ ___

    ___ ___ ___ ___ ___ (to copy a signature for fraudulent reasons)   ___ ___ ___

    ___ ___   ___ ___ ___ ___ (the metallic ringing sound of a bell)

    ___ ___ ___ ___ ___   ___ ___ ___

10. DANGEROUS   ___ ___ ___ ___ ___ ___ ___   ___ ___ ___

    ___ ___   ___ ___ ___ ___

11. ORANGE   ___ ___   ___ ___ ___   ___ ___ ___ ___ ___

    ___ ___ ___ ___ ___ ___ (Malay word for 'man' and the first part of the name of an ape)

    ___ ___ ___ ___ ___

12. MESSAGE   ___ ___ ___ ___   ___ ___ ___ ___ (herb used in cooking)

    ___ ___ ___ ___ ___

13. BASKETBALL   ___ ___   ___ ___ ___ ___ (to lie in pleasant warmth, sunbathe)

    ___ ___ ___ ___   ___ ___ ___ ___ ___ ___ ___

14. SWALLOW   ___ ___ ___ ___ ___   ___ ___ ___ ___   ___ ___ ___

    ___ ___ ___ ___ ___ ___ (to roll about in mud)   ___ ___ ___

15. STATIONMASTER   ___ ___ ___ ___ ___ ___   ___ ___ ___ ___

    ___ ___ ___ ___ ___ ___ (a type of flower)   ___ ___ ___ ___ ___ ___ ___

Spelling Activity – Editing

Each sentence below contains two spelling mistakes.

Circle the incorrect words and write them correctly on the lines provided.
See the example that has been done for you.

1. Anne was a verry happy littel girl. _____ _____

2. She had enjoid her holliday on the farm, _____ _____
    but she was glad to be going home.

3. Mother went to the window to biy the ticketts. _____ _____

4. At laast the <u>trane</u> came. _____ ____train____

5. They got on bord and found a seate. _____ _____

6. A strainge boy sat neckst to them. _____ _____

7. He had an old sacke whith him. _____ _____

8. He openned it and pulled out a sock, _____ _____
    sandwitches and tiny bits of string.

9. 'They call me Bruce,' he sed, smileing. _____ _____

10. 'Would you licke a peice of bread?' _____ _____

11. 'No, thank you,' Anne ansered quitely. _____ _____

12. The boy begain beating a kettel drum and _____ _____
    blowing a horn.

13. Anne and her mother were plesed when he _____ _____
    got off at the following staton.

14. The rest of the jorney was reely quiet. _____ _____

15. There stop was the forth along the track. _____ _____

Write five words with each ending:

ark _____

ast _____

ink _____

ion _____

Draw a word train like the one below.

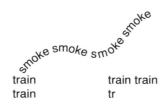

Story Editing

Before any piece of written work is published, it must be read for the purpose of finding and correcting possible mistakes. In the story below, each line contains two mistakes. *If a word has been misspelt, underline it and write the correct spelling on the line. If a word has been used incorrectly, circle it and write the correct word on the line.* The first line has been done for you.

The Three Little Pigs

		upon	were
1.	Once <u>apon</u> a time there (was) three little pigs.		
2.	Thay lived in a cotage deep in the forest with		
3.	Mother Pig. There names were John, andrew and Barry.		
4.	The pigs et and ate. They grew and grew. Won day, when		
5.	they coming home from football training, Mrs Pig sed,		
6.	'Youse are getten too big for this house. You must go		
7.	out into the wide werld and seak your fortunes'.		
8.	'Give us a break, Mum!' cryed Andrew in alarm as he puts		
9.	another steak in the barbequeque.		
10.	Four a while they taked turns sleeping outside		
11.	but at last the time come to went.		
12.	'Dont forget to right,' sobbed Mother Pig, wiping back		
13.	gaint teers.		
14.	It was the best thing they could of did. John is		
15.	marriage and is the chief dishwasher at a mcgurgle's		
16.	resturant. Andrew is a docter and Barry is a		
17.	sheep farmer at yorkshire.		
18.	I hop this story teaches you a leson. Don't be too		
19.	upset when things are'nt going your way. Keep you're		
20.	chin up and puff your chess out. Pull your stumick in		
21.	and stand up straightly. While your at it, tuck your shirt		
22.	in and combe your hair. Check that you have too socks		
23.	the same color on your feet. If you follow them golden		
24.	rules you could be retired at twenny with an block		
25.	of flats in Liverpool's beautiful Mersey River.		

Story Editing II

The story below badly needs editing. Each line contains two mistakes and, in some cases, an additional punctuation mistake. *If a word has been misspelt, underline it and write the correct spelling on the line. If a word has been used incorrectly, circle it and write the correct word on the line. If there is a (P) at the end of a line there is a punctuation error. Put a line through the error and write the correction nearby.* The first line has been done for you.

The Three Little Pigs - High Road to Adventure

		was	for
1.	At last It (were) time <u>fore</u> the three little pigs (P)		
2.	to leaving home and seek there fortunes? (P)		
3.	The first Pig strided into the unknowen. (P)		
4.	He traveled far, and widde. (P)		
5.	He swum rageing Rivers. (P)		
6.	he climed snow-capped moutains. (P)		
7.	He cross hot desserts? (P)		
8.	He hacked his way thru Steamy jungels. (P)		
9.	In this time he face, great dangerous. (P)		
10.	sharks try to bit him.(P)		
11.	A mountain goat tride to but Him. (P)		
12.	angry camels spitted and hist at him. (P)		
13.	Once day he seen a little house on the		
14.	prairie inn the distants.		
15.	He was verry thin anD week. (P)		
16.	He drug hisself to the front Porch. (P)		
17.	A familair face geets Him. (P)		
18.	'pedro!' shreeked Muther Pig. (P)		
19.	Was it an dreem. (P)		
20.	he pincht hisself. (P)		
21.	'yow!' screemed the littel pig. (P)		
22.	It weren't no dream.		
23.	One of his trotter's was shorta then the other. (P)		
24.	He had walkt in a enormous circle.		

Writing Sentences

We usually don't think in perfectly formed sentences. Instead we have 'flashes' of ideas. To share these ideas with others we must write them in sentences and follow the rules that govern written expression. *Expand these 'flashes' into sentences on another piece of paper. In some cases you may need more than one sentence to say it all.*

1. woke up - green spots on tongue - mother called doctor - in bed for two weeks

2. two children playing - ball onto road - a lucky escape from serious injury - learnt a lesson

3. bought seeds - watered - pumpkin pie

4. first game for school team - nervous - scored winning goal/try/run - congratulations and cheers from team-mates

5. weekend - out of bed at 6.00 a.m. - rainy, freezing cold - back to bed

6. fishing with Dad - big bite - five kilogram fish

7. sent to headteacher - very worried - given award for outstanding work

8. going to school - sick magpie - broken wing - cared for - visits family often now

9. countdown - blast off - excited - destination the Purple Planet

10. worked hard - improved all marks - good report card - Mum and Dad very proud

11. cooked breakfast - washed up - cleaned room - Mum surprised - Mother's Day

12. prince - princess - kiss - explosion and lots of smoke - turned into toads

13. very dry weather - thoughtless smoker - lighted cigarette thrown out of car window - dry grass - thousands of hectares of burnt moorland - many animals killed

14. visited zoo with brother/sister - gorilla escaped - trail of peanuts back to cage - award for bravery

15. washed hands - switched off light - shock - wet hands - learnt important lesson

16. exploring teacher's storeroom - unscrewed jar - bumped - varnish all over uniform

17. lost in desert - oasis in the distance - ran towards it - learnt meaning of the word 'mirage' - luckily rescued by camel caravan

18. hamburger in polystyrene carton - thrown out - discarded at tip - broken down - years of pollution - by destroying the ozone layer - many people affected by skin cancer, cataracts and weakened immune system

19. about to enter door - heard big brother shriek in terror - mouse in kitchen

20. piano practice - more piano practice - improve playing - now realise benefits of practice

21. bike riding - showing off - no hands! - no feet! - no teeth and two cauliflower ears

22. off to the beach - don't forget to use sun cream says Mum - why does she nag? - didn't use sun cream - know why she nags now

23. Jack and Jill - descended steep climb - grip slip - Jack flat on back - vinegar and brown paper recommended by doctor not used in such cases

24. Christmas Day - up early - presents? - Santa and elves on strike

25. very hungry after school - straight to fridge when home - gulped down what looked like meat loaf - Rover frothing at mouth and visibly upset - realised my mistake

26. alarm went off - jumped out of bed - no breakfast - missed the bus - late for school - worried about what the teacher would say - sneaked into the class

27. thinking of ideas for story - no great ideas - decided to do something else

Matching Pairs

Put in a word to complete each matching pair. *Study the first pair and try to work out how the words are linked, then complete the second pair using the same link.*

Example: forest, trees, book, <u>pages</u>

1. lawn, grass, wig _____
2. smell, nose, see _____
3. Donald Duck, Daisy Duck, Mickey Mouse _____
4. people, houses, birds _____
5. triangle, three, hexagon _____
6. cap, head, ring _____
7. six, even, nine _____
8. tree, wood, brick _____
9. cloud, sky, earthworm _____
10. car passenger, seat belt, bicycle rider _____
11. USA, President, Great Britain _____
12. comic, pictures, dictionary _____
13. trousers, pocket, kangaroo _____
14. duck, bill, person _____
15. husband, wife, brother _____
16. orange, peel, peanut _____
17. Wight, island, Africa _____
18. tea, leaf, coffee _____
19. baker, bread, butcher _____
20. cow, horns, elephant _____
21. football, goal, cricket _____
22. glove, hand, shoe _____
23. dusk, evening, dawn _____
24. trout, river, frog _____
25. Ian Botham, cricket, Sebastian Coe _____
26. armchair, lounge, refrigerator _____

27. pilot, aeroplane, chauffeur _____
28. Shakespeare, plays, Mozart _____
29. Harbour Bridge, Sydney, Big Ben _____
30. polar bear, Arctic, penguin _____
31. headline, front page, sports news _____
32. fox, fur, plaice _____
33. water, bottle, money _____
34. catch, caught, run _____
35. honey, sweet, vinegar _____
36. tram, tracks, car _____
37. summer, sweat, winter _____
38. cabbage, round, banana _____
39. rose, red, panther _____
40. dog, kennel, bee _____
41. America's Cup, yachting Davis Cup _____
42. mattress, springs, water bed _____
43. coconut, tree, grape _____
44. Union Jack, Great Britain, Stars and Stripes _____
45. volcano, lava, storm cloud _____
46. Wellington, New Zealand, Belfast _____
47. bandage, wound, blanket _____
48. note, music, number _____
49. fan, wind, radiator _____
50. iguana, lizard, python _____

Make up some of our own matching pairs and try them on your friends.

_____

_____

_____

_____

_____

Rhyming Couples

The answers to the clues below rhyme. *Try to work them out.*
The first one is done for you.

1. ancient / precious metal   <u>o l d</u> / <u>g o l d</u>

2. large / porker   ___ ___ ___ / ___ ___ ___

3. boring / seabird   ___ ___ ___ ___ / ___ ___ ___

4. giddy / short for Elizabeth   ___ ___ ___ ___ / ___ ___ ___

5. happy / father   ___ ___ ___ / ___ ___ ___

6. pleasant / rodents   ___ ___ ___ ___ / ___ ___ ___

7. not warm / silly person   ___ ___ ___ ___ / ___ ___ ___

8. not more / untidiness   ___ ___ ___ ___ / ___ ___ ___

9. heaven / not low   ___ ___ ___ / ___ ___ ___

10. little / round thing   ___ ___ ___ ___ / ___ ___ ___

11. not sensible / young female horse   ___ ___ ___ ___ ___ / ___ ___ ___ ___

12. better than all the others / nuisance   ___ ___ ___ ___ / ___ ___ ___ ___

13. furry / winged character in children's stories   ___ ___ ___ ___ ___ / ___ ___ ___ ___ ___

14. distant / sun   ___ ___ ___ / ___ ___ ___

15. not thin / baked stone used in building   ___ ___ ___ ___ ___ / ___ ___ ___ ___ ___

16. less tall / girl child   ___ ___ ___ ___ ___ / ___ ___ ___ ___ ___

17. pretty plant / strength   ___ ___ ___ ___ ___ / ___ ___ ___ ___

18. from Switzerland / girl's title   ___ ___ ___ ___ ___ / ___ ___ ___

19. to heat for eating / you read it   ___ ___ ___ ___ / ___ ___ ___ ___

20. a lot of ships / road   ___ ___ ___ ___ / ___ ___ ___ ___ ___

21. pancake shape / talk   ___ ___ ___ ___ / ___ ___ ___ ___

22. useful / short for Andrew   ___ ___ ___ ___ / ___ ___ ___

23. part of you that thinks / ditch   ___ ___ ___ ___ ___ / ___ ___ ___ ___

24. sea creature / plate   ___ ___ ___ ___ / ___ ___ ___ ___

25. to put off / horses eat this   ___ ___ ___ ___ ___ / ___ ___ ___

26. a close buddy / to fold something over   ___ ___ ___ ___ ___ / ___ ___ ___ ___

27. you go here to learn / place to swim   ___ ___ ___ ___ ___ / ___ ___ ___ ___

Make up some of your own rhyming couples.

_____

_____

_____

By dropping one letter at a time in the words below, you form new words. *See if you can get down to just one single-letter word.*

Example: <u>c r a n e</u>   <u>c a n e</u>   <u>c a n</u>   <u>a n</u>   <u>a</u>

S W I N E   _ _ _ _   _ _ _   _ _   _

S P O I L T   _ _ _ _ _   _ _ _ _   _ _ _   _ _   _

B L I N K   _ _ _ _   _ _ _   _ _   _

S C R E A M   _ _ _ _ _   _ _ _ _   _ _ _   _ _   _

H E A R T   _ _ _ _   _ _ _   _ _   _

F L A T T E R   _ _ _ _ _ _   _ _ _ _ _   _ _ _ _   _ _ _
                  _ _   _

B R A I N   _ _ _ _   _ _ _   _ _   _

A P A R T   _ _ _ _   _ _ _   _ _   _

G R A S P   _ _ _ _   _ _ _   _ _   _

S P L A S H   _ _ _ _ _   _ _ _ _   _ _ _   _ _   _

C R E A T E D   _ _ _ _ _ _   _ _ _ _ _   _ _ _ _   _ _ _
                  _ _   _

S N O W I N G   _ _ _ _ _ _   _ _ _ _ _   _ _ _ _   _ _ _
                  _ _   _

Words in Words

Each word below has an article of clothing concealed in it.
Find the hidden word and write it next to the word in which it is concealed.

C H A T T E R   _ _ _ _

I N V E S T M E N T   _ _ _ _ _

D U S T I E S T   _ _ _ _

D O G L O V E R   _ _ _ _ _ _

E S C A P E E   _ _ _ _ _

I N C A P A C I T Y   _ _ _ _

U N S U I T A B L E   _ _ _ _ _ _

A D D R E S S   _ _ _ _ _ _

S H O R T S T O P   _ _ _ _ _ _ _

'Pin' Words

Find the words that fit the clues below. All begin with 'P I N'.

This P I N means to squeeze hard: _ _ _ _ _ _

This P I N means a colour: _ _ _ _ _

This P I N is a type of horse: _ _ _ _ _ _

This P I N is a pattern of lines: _ _ _ _ _ _ _ _

This P I N is a rock formation: _ _ _ _ _ _ _ _ _

This P I N is a type of wood: _ _ _ _ _

This P I N is a entertainment game: _ _ _ _ _ _ _

Choose three consecutive letters from each word below. *Put these bits and pieces together to form a word that belongs to the category.*

Example: <u>aut</u>omatic / s<u>hor</u>e = author

A. **Occupations**
1. dockyard / tractor = _____
2. stain / glorious = _____
3. insect / concrete / diary = _____
4. starch / hitting / respect = _____
5. careful / opening / butter = _____
6. apology / notice / mango = _____
7. skilful / undid / very = _____
8. laneway / usage / centre = _____
9. claws / prayer = _____
10. phone / toggle / grape / father = _____

B. **Countries**
1. sausage / traffic / brilliant = _____
2. crust / Asian = _____
3. ignore / railway = _____
4. swept / hidden = _____
5. infra-red / Vincent = _____
6. impolite / sandwich = _____
7. pantry / llama = _____
8. remind / alone / Siamese = _____
9. ogre / enlist / panda = _____
10. cargo / spent / inaccurate = _____
11. adventure / donkey = _____

C. **Counties and Towns** (use an atlas to help)
1. suspicious / sextant = _____
2. belong / undone = _____
3. surprise / grey = _____
4. adorable / settler = _____
5. break / inconsistent = _____
6. redundant / redeem = _____
7. soldier / champion = _____
8. bandit / angora = _____
9. awoke / running = _____
10. bossanova / stones = _____

Try to work out the familiar word, phrases or figure of speech below. Use the example to show you how to find the solution.

inside

H A H A N D N D	ONCE 2.30 p.m.	
Hand in hand		

p i g *p i g* *p i g*	 *i* — *i*	**o** **u** **t**

r **o** **r o a d s** **d** **s**	*5 + 5 is*	ground railway

PROM / ISE	**lands** **Scottish**	*w a t e r*

aircraft 	w e e k e n d	**TEXASUTAHOHIOIOWA**

Colour the pictures when you have finished or while you are thinking. See if you can make up some of these yourself.

Broken Titles

Scott is sometimes forgetful when he writes things down. Sometimes he forgets to leave spaces between words and other times he leaves spaces where they do not belong. Below, he has written the names of some of his favourite stories and songs(*).

Can you write them correctly for him?

1. Cha rliean dthechoco latefactor y = <u>Charlie and the Chocolate Factory.</u>

2. Snowwh itean dthese vendw arfs = _____

3. Wi ndint hewil lo ws = _____

4. Tre as ureis land = _____

5. Jam esandt hegia ntpeac h = _____

6. Thewon derfu lwiza rdofoz = _____

7. Jour neytothecen treoft heea rth = _____

8. Bla ckbeau ty = _____

9. Theta leofpet errab bit = _____

10. Gul liverstr avels = _____

11. Thom asth etan ken gine = _____

12. Theli onth ewitc handth ewardr o be = _____

13. Theti memac hine = _____

14. T het wit s = _____

15. Lit tlere dridin gho od = _____

16. Fla tsta nley = _____

17. Twe ntytho usand le ague sun derth esea = _____

18. Theh obb it = _____

19. Oldma cdo nald ha dafa rm * = _____

20. Sco tla ndth ebra ve * = _____

21. Ji ngl ebe lls * = _____

22. Wal tzin gmat ild a * = _____

23. Goo dkin gwenc eslas * = _____

24. Te ngre enbot tl es * = _____

25. Godsa veth eque en * = _____

26. Wewis hyou ame rryc hri st mas * = _____

27. Tw ink letw ink lelit tlest ar * = _____

28. Am a zing gr ace * = _____

29. Ol dlan gsyne* = _____

30. Jo ytoth ewor ld * = _____

Headline News

Match the headlines and newspaper articles below with the fairytales or nursery rhymes they stand for. *Colour the answer squares as you match answers.*

Jack and the Beanstalk   What can the matter be?   Hey Diddle-Diddle   Peter Piper

The Three Bears   Georgie Peorgie   The Pied Piper   Wee Willie Winkie   Cock Robin

Solomon Grundy   Ding, Dong, Bell   Twelve Days of Christmas   The Mulberry Bush   Chicken Licken   Cinderella

Pinocchio   The Ugly Duckling   Simple Simon   Jack and Jill   Little Bo Peep

1. Sky not falling says leading scientist _____

2. Dame Dob wins Nobel prize for her miracle cure - vinegar and brown paper _____

3. Porridge thief finally caught _____

4. Family forced to move into bigger house - too many Christmas presents _____

5. Huge pepper harvest - more pickers wanted _____

6. Glass slipper owner found _____

7. Shooting tragedy - 'I didn't know it was loaded,' says sparrow _____

8. UFO identified as cow _____

9. Strange claim - 'I am really a puppet but I don't have a wooden heart,' says boy _____

10. Johnny finally comes home - not lost, just at the fair all the time _____

11. Shock death - 'He achieved more in a week than some people do in a lifetime,' says grieving wife _____

12. Swan reveals - My dreadful childhood: 'They said I was ugly!' _____

13. Brave boy saves cat _____

14. Bargain of the century! Cow sold for a handful of seeds. Mother to appeal _____

15. Cold, frosty weather to continue _____

16. Boys chase phantom kisser away - 'We nearly caught him!' _____

17. Sheep found but tails still missing _____

18. Free concert in Hamelin on the banks of the River Weser _____

19. Prowler held on nuisance charge. Mother tells: 'He frightened my children and woke the baby!' _____

20. Hard times hit pie sellers - 'Many people can't even afford a pie!' says distraught pie bar owner _____

Answer Page

Nouns - page 1.

[Crossword grid with answers including: TEACHER, SCIENCE, INK, HEALTH, SPORT, DESK, BOOKS, COMPASS, GEOMETRY, PLAYGROUND, PEN, CHALK, PASTE, SPELLING, STUDENTS, MAGNET, READINGBOOK, MATHEMATICS, HOMEWORK]

a = 12, b = 1, c = 16, d = 5, e = 8, f = 19, g = 14, h = 3, i = 7, j is not used, k = 26, l = 17, m = 9, n = 4, o = 2, p = 15, q is not used, r = 18, s = 10, t = 6, u = 11, v is not used, w = 22, x = 13, y = 20, z is not used.

Singular and Plural - page 2.

From the first word (centre right) to the last word (bottom right corner) - foxes, tables, chairs, babies, oxen, teeth, potatoes, tomatoes, leaves, cats, wolves, classrooms, aeroplanes, mice, horses, children, geese, feet, dwarfs, toes, roofs, sisters, elves, peas, pianos, valleys, knives, pillows, heroes, women, spoonfuls, men, passers-by, coins, thieves, chiefs, echoes, hands, shoes, fleas, cabbages, bees, flowers, cities, dreams, socks, oceans, ankles, gardens, shells, baskets, shelves, saucers, cups, kangaroos, elephants, mosquitoes.

Verbs - page 3.

[Crossword grid with answers including: LISTENS, PAY, GROWLED, SAW, SEE, SCRATCHED, HEAR, SAID, BOUGHT, EXPLAIN, SPOKE, DID, RAN, FLY, HOP, FIZZLE, JUMPED, SAT, SAY, ANSWERED, LEAPT, FLOW, CATCH, DROP, STOOD, PINCH, GREW, SAG, HAD, LOOK, LICK, TALK, LIED, THINK]

a = 9, b = 6, c = 16, d = 20, e = 1, f = 19, g = 10, h = 17, i = 3, j 12, k = 18, l = 21, m = 11, n = 22, o = 2, p = 5, q is not used, r = 23, s = 4, t = 7, u = 26, v = 24, w = 25, x = 8, y = 14, z = 15.

Verbs - Tense - page 4.

From the first word (centre right) to the last word (bottom right) - ran, jumped, cried, swam, walked, talked, wrote, sat, stood, laughed, drove, yelled, smiled, had, kicked, ate, looked, thought, played, stood, worked, spoke, grew, listened, sang, drank, drew, went, said, screamed, kissed, looked, listened, sank, cleaned, slept, told, climbed, opened, called, boiled, studied, watched, floated, started, dropped, closed, followed, lived, invited, used, asked, answered, sailed, patted, replied, showed, galloped, caught, destroyed, hopped, coughed, finished.

Adverbs - page 6.

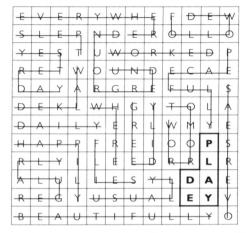

Adverbs of manner - played, happily - slept, peacefully
Adverbs of time - flies, usually - walked, yesterday.
Adverbs of place - followed, everywhere - worked, underground.
1. daily, 2. tomorrow, 3. regularly, 4. greedily, 5. beautifully, 6. where, 7. overseas.

Personal Pronouns - page 7.

In order from 1 to 14 - I, my, me, his, himself, she, her, you, yourselves, they, themselves, their, we, ourselves, our, us, it, he, him, its, itself, mine, yours, them, your.
Picture - An Oceanliner.

Nouns, Pronouns, Adjectives, Verbs and Adverbs - page 8.

Teacher to check the underwater scene.

Prepositions - page 9.

1. through 2. down 3. along 4. across 5. around 6. in 7. towards 8. near 9. to 10. underneath 11. against 12. into 13. below 14. under 15. beneath 16. from 17. over 18. between.

Contractions - page 10.

From the first (bottom left corner) to the last word - aren't, wasn't, we'll, don't, it'll, we're, isn't, won't, he's, who's, didn't, I'm, haven't, it's, shan't, where's, mustn't, you'll, there's, you've, couldn't, he'll, we've, wouldn't, she'll, I've, would've, shouldn't, could've, weren't, you're, she's, that's, they've, doesn't, they're, can't, I ll, let's, hadn't, they'll, what's, hasn't, should've, aren't.

Punctuation - page 11.

Teacher to correct.

Using the Right Word - page 12.

1. did 2. saw 3. done 4. seen 5. sung 6. sang 7. drank 8. drunk 9. swam 10. swum 11. eaten 12. ate 13. begun 14. began 15. gone 16. went 17. broken 18. broke 19. flown 20. flew 21. shaken 22. shook 23. forgotten 24. forgot 25. written 26. wrote 27. ran 28. run 29. spoken 30. spoke 31. rung 32. rang 33. fallen 34. fell.

Spoonerisms - page 13.

Around the House - backgarden, dishwasher, dining room, carport, bathroom, kitchen sink, roof tiles, linen cupboard, back door.

The Circus and Fair - balloon sellers, lion tamer, ghost train, roller coaster, coconut shy, big top, show ring, sawdust, Ferris wheel.

At School - playground, pencil case, maths book, textbooks, skipping rope, chalkboard, schoolchild, canteen, multiplication tables.

At the Beach - lifesavers, beach towel, surfboard, bathing costume, seagulls, high tide, sand dunes, sunbathers, rock pools.

Animals - Bulldog, reindeer, termite, French poodle, sheep dog, tomcat, queen bee, ladybird, cockroach.

Famous People - Charles Dickens, Florence Nightingale, Samuel Plimsoll, John Lennon, Margaret Thatcher, Lord Baden Powell, Douglas Bader, Mahatma Gandhi, Leonardo de Vinci.

The Drawings - traffic lights, footpath, bus stop, neon lights, taxicab.

Spoonerisms II - page 14.

Sports - rugby league, badminton, lawn tennis, volleyball, show jumping, tenpin bowling, long jump, shot-put, triple jump.

Towns and Cities in the United Kingdom - Birmingham, Middleborough, Kilmarnock, Halifax, Sunderland, Belfast, Bristol, Durham, Shrewsbury, Norwich, Nottingham, Chipping Norton, Cardiff, Matlock, Winchester, Glastonbury, Southampton, Cambridge.

Capital Cities from around the World- London, Canberra, Madrid, Copenhagen, Helsinki, Bangkok, Baghdad, New Delhi, Lisbon.

Famous Landmarks and Places - Black Forest, Stonehenge, Suez Canal, Hadrian's Wall, Ben Nevis, Windsor Castle, Scapa Flow, Buckingham Palace, London Bridge, Mull of Kintyre, Trafalgar Square, Cliffs of Dover, Westminster Abbey, Lake District.

Characters from Fiction Stories - Rumpelstiltskin, Noddy and Big Ears, Sleeping Beauty, Tom Thumb, Three Bears, King Midas, Sinbad, Puss in Boots, Prince Charming, Snow White.

Analogies - page 15.

1. Queen Bee/Drone/Worker Bee 2. water 3. spots 4. hat 5. bill 6. Batman/Robin 7. boat/yacht/ship 8. whale 9. smoking 10. finger 11. tracks 12. spaceship/rocket 13. sheep 14. Australia 15. yolk 16. book 17. The Wolf 18. student/school children 19. tree/water 20. horse 21. London 22. music 23. Paris 24. flag 25. green 26. tusks 27. brought 28. school 29. mine 30. scales 31. two 32. air 33. Princess 34. Samson 35. black.

Similes - page 16.

1. dog 2. churchmouse 3. bat 4. ditchwater 5. ghost 6. Methuselah 7. hills 8. pancake 9. ox 10. mother 11. bee 12. hatter 13. fox 14. Solomon 15. owl 16. Punch 17. pig 18. swan 19. Job 20. mouse 21. eel 22. picture 23. sin 24. mule.

Proverbs - page 17.

1. leak, ship 2. silence 3. birds, flock 4. vessels, sound 5. cooks, broth 6. bird, bush 7. enough, feast 8. water, dry 9. workman, tools 10. sauce 11. seen, heard 12. truth 13. early bird, worm 14. bed, lie 15. a'sorrowing, a'borrowing.

Extra Activities - 1. four 2. seven 3. nine

Anagrams - page 18.

1. each, ache 2. gum, mug 3. much, chum, 4. won, now, own 5. spit, tips, pits 6. peels, sleep 7. pest, step, pets 8. sail, Lisa, Isla, ails 9. tuna, a nut, aunt 10. flea, leaf 11. heads, shade, a shed 12. pains, Spain 13. oaks, soak 14. hoes, shoe, hose, 15. tens, nest, nets, sent 16. warder, drawer, reward 17. tames, teams, mates, meats, steam 18. trade, rated, tread 19. paces, space, capes 20. dawn, wand.

Tautology - page 19.

1. while he was still alive 2. me, myself, personally 3. again 4. frozen 5. regularly 6. ever 7. no hair 8. stone dead 9. filthy 10. and cloudless 11. very 12. over the opposition's goal line 13. more and more 14. down 15. completely 16. really 17. day 18. single 19. on my hand 20. forward 21. enough 22. big 23. beautifully 24. before noon 25. before scoring any runs 26. untrue 27. every time 28. distant 29. dangerously 30. painfully 31. on top of the water 32. and cookies.

Compound Words - page 20.

1. for 2. head 3. weather 4. mad 5. over 6. steel 7. baby 8. some 9. hot 10. green 11. wind 12. door 13. lemon 14. wide 15. horse 16. extra 17. nut 18. post 19. church 20. civil 21. down 22. glass 23. pole 24. smoke 25. sky 26. hay 27. ship 28. water 29. bone 30. granny.

Well Known Opposites - page 21.

1. Black Beauty 2. lifesaver 3. understand 4. outback 5. highlight 6. leftover 7. legend 8. hand me down 9. income 10. Sitting Bull 11. breakfast 12. fullback 13. round up 14. give in 15. handstand 16. good day 17. fallout 18. father 19. nightmare 20. Little Women.

Alphabetical Building Blocks - page 22.

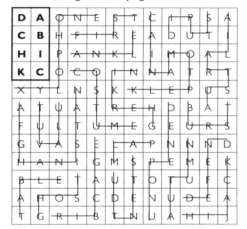

1. dabchick 2. table 3. hijack 4. ghost 5. ribcage 6. defend 7. autumn 8. stupid 9. first 10. ankle 11. costume 12. xylophone 13. Afghanistan 14. unopened 15. palm 16. student 17. Australia 18. Tuvalu 19. gherkin 20. burst 21. kleptomaniac.

Alphabet Soup - page 23.

1. p 2. x 3. y 4. q 5. h 6. z 7. j 8. u 9. o 10. s 11. r 12. g 13. t 14. m 15. d 16. f 17. i 18. k 19. w 20. b 21. c 22. a 23. e 24. l 25. v 26. n.

Letter Sounds - gg, mt, ii, gi, r, ok, dj.

Following Directions - page 24.

Message One - The Sheriff is Coming!
Message Two - No I'm not!

Worm Words - page 25.

Exercise A - 1. utter 2. remark 3. announce 4. earbash 5. comment 6. jabber 7. exclaim 8. gossip 9. grumble 10. murmur.

Exercise B - 1. saunter 2. shamble 3. lumber 4. trample 5. stagger 6. parade.

Exercise C - 1. disgraceful 2. appalling 3. unworthy 4. abysmal 5. terrible 6. digusting.

Exercise D - 1. capital 2. wonderful 3. exquisite 4. outstanding 5. excellent 6. marvellous.

Earthworms Worksheet - page 27.

Exercise A - 1. burrows, soil 2. 24 hours 3. decayed plant matter 4. night 5. hermaphrodites 6. segments 7. chaetae 8. saddle, clitellum 9. cocoons for young worms 10. compost heap.

Exercise B - 1. wormery 2. fertiliser 3. artificial 4. leisure 5. uncomplicated 6. producing 7. contracted 8. section 9. regularly 10. creatures.

Exercise C - 1. farmers, gardeners 2. soil, plant scraps, grass clippings and leaves.

Exercise D - nowadays, burrows, cast, usually, leisure

Exercise E - 1. night, inside burrow 2. cocoons for young worms

Words in Words - page 28.

1. sun, shine, suns, shin, in 2. hill, chill, ill, hilly 3. dragon, fly, rag, go, on, drag, ago 4. paper, new, news, spa, per 5. fat, her, the, he, at 6. screw, driver, river, drive, crew 7. every, thing, thin, ever, very, Eve 8. over, flow, wing, flowing, owing, in, overflow, low, win, lowing 9. forget, get, tin, forge, for, ting, getting, or 10. danger, us, an, anger 11. or, on, range, orang, rang, ran, age 12. mess, sage, sag, age, me 13. as, bask, ball, ask, basket 14. allow, wall, low, wallow, all 15. master, as, on, aster, station

Spelling Activity - Editing - page 29.

1. very, little 2. enjoyed, holiday 3. buy, tickets 4. last, train 5. board, seat 6. strange, next 7. sack, with 8. opened, sandwiches 9. said, smiling 10. like, piece 11. answered, quietly 12. began, kettle 13. pleased, station 14. journey, really 15. their, fourth.

Story Editing - page 30.

The Three Little Pigs - 1. upon, were 2. they, cottage 3. their, Andrew 4. ate, One 5. came, said 6. you, getting 7. world, seek 8. cried, put 9. on, barbeque 10. for, took 11. came, go 12. Don't, write 13. giant, tears 14. have, done 15. married, McGurgle's 16. restaurant, doctor 17. in, Yorkshire 18. hope, lesson 19. aren't, your 20. chest, stomach 21. straight, you're 22. comb, two 23. colour, those 24. twenty, a 25. on, Liverpool's.

Story Editing II - page 31.

The Three Little Pigs - High Road to Adventure - 1. was, for 2. leave, their, full stop for ? 3. strode, unknown, small p in pig 4. travelled, wide, no comma 5. swam, raging, small r in rivers 6. climbed, mountains, start with capital H

7. crossed, deserts, full stop not ? 8. through, jungles, small s in steamy 9. faced, dangers, no comma 10. tried, bite, start with capital S 11. tried, butt, small h in him 12. spat, hissed, start with capital A 13. One, saw 14. in, distance 15. very, weak, small d in and 16. dragged, himself, small p in porch 17. familiar, greeted, small h in him 18. shrieked, Mother, capital P for Pedro 19. a, dream, ? 20. pinched, himself, start with capital H 21. screamed, little, start with capital Y 22. wasn't, a 23. shorter, than, no ' in trotters 24. walked, an

Writing Sentences - page 32.

Teacher to correct.

Matching Pairs - page 33.

1. hair 2. eye 3. Minnie Mouse 4. nests 5. six 6. finger 7. odd 8. clay 9. soil 10. helmet 11. Prime Minister 12. words 13. pouch 14. mouth 15. sister 16. shell 17. continent 18. bean 19. meat 20. tusks 21. run 22. foot 23. morning 24. swamp 25. running 26. kitchen 27. car 28. music 29. London 30. Antarctic 31. back page 32. scales 33. bank 34. ran 35. sour 36. road 37. shiver 38. long 39. black 40. hive 41. tennis 42. water 43. vine 44. USA 45. rain 46. Northern Ireland 47. bed 48. mathematics 49. heat 50. snake.

Rhyming Couples - page 34.

1. old/gold 2. big/pig 3. dull/gull 4. dizzy/Lizzy 5. glad/Dad 6. nice/mice 7. cool/fool 8. less/mess 9. sky/high 10. small/ball 11. silly/filly 12. best/pest 13. hairy/fairy 14. far/star 15. thick/brick 16. shorter/daughter 17. flower/power 18. Swiss/miss 19. cook/book 20. fleet/street 21. flat/chat 22. handy/Andy 23. brain/drain 24. fish/dish 25. delay/hay 26. friend/bend 27. school/pool.

Thinking Time - page 35.

swine - wine, win, in, I *spoilt* - spilt, spit, sit, it, I *blink* - link, ink, in, I *scream* - cream, cram, ram, am, a *heart* - heat, hat, at, a *flatter* - latter, later, late, ate, at, a *brain* - rain, ran, an, a *apart* - part, art, at, a *grasp* - gasp, asp, as, a *splash* - slash, sash, ash, as, a *created* - create, crate, rate, rat, at, a *snowing* - sowing, owing, wing, win, in, I

Words in Words - hat, vest, tie, glove, cape, cap, suit, dress, shorts

'Pin' Words - pinch, pink, pinto, pinstripe, pinnacle, pine, pinball

Bits and Pieces - page 36.

Occupations - 1. doctor 2. tailor 3. secretary 4. architect 5. carpenter 6. policeman 7. skindiver 8. newsagent 9. lawyer 10. photographer.

Countries - 1. Australia 2. Russia 3. Norway 4. Sweden 5. France 6. Poland 7. Panama 8. Indonesia 9. Greenland 10. Argentina 11. Turkey.

Counties and Towns - 1. Sussex 2. London 3. Surrey 4. Dorset 5. Brecon 6. Dundee 7. Oldham 8. Bangor 9. Woking

10. Boston.

Unfamiliar, Familair Words and Phrases - page 37.

Hand in hand, once upon a time, inside out, Three Little Pigs, bright eyes, outside, crossroads, tennis, underground railway, broken promise, Scottish highlands, underwater, aircraft carrier, long weekend, United States of America.

Broken Titles - page 38.

1. Charlie and the Chocolate Factory 2. Snow White and the Seven Dwarfs 3. Wind in the Willows 4. Treasure Island 5. James and the Giant Peach 6. The Wonderful Wizard of Oz 7. Journey to the Centre of the Earth 8. Black Beauty 9. The Tales of Peter Rabbit 10. Gulliver's Travels 11. Thomas the Tank Engine 12. The Lion, the Witch and the Wardrobe 13. The Time Machine 14. The Twits 15. Little Red Riding Hood 16. Flat Stanley 17. Twenty Thousand Leagues under the Sea 18. The Hobbit 19. Old MacDonald had a Farm 20. Scotland the Brave 21. Jingle Bells 22. Waltzing Matilda 23. Good King Wenceslas 24. Ten Green Bottles 25. God Save the Queen 26. We Wish You a Merry Christmas 27. Twinkle Twinkle Little Star 28. Amazing Grace 29. Old Lang Syne 30. Joy to the World.

Headline News - page 39.

1. Chicken Licken 2. Jack and Jill 3. The Three Bears 4. Twelve Days of Christmas 5. Peter Piper 6. Cinderella 7. Cock Robin 8. Hey Diddle Diddle 9. Pinnochio 10. What Can the Matter be? 11. Solomon Grundy 12. The Ugly Duckling 13. Ding, Dong, Bell 14. Jack and the Beanstalk 15. The Mulberry Bush 16. Georgie Porgie 17. Little Bo Peep 18. The Pied Piper 19. Wee Willie Winkie 20. Simple Simon.